MH00577706

Ludwig van
BEETHOVEN

Mass in C
Op. 86

(Carl Reinecke)

Vocal Score
Klavierauszug

SERENISSIMA MUSIC, INC.
Masters Music Publications, Inc., Sole Selling Agent

CONTENTS

ORCHESTRA

2 Flutes, 2 Oboes, 2 Clarinets, 2 Bassoons
4 Horns, 2 Trumpets
Timpani
Organ
Violin I, Violin II, Viola, Violoncello, Double Bass

Duration: ca. 50 minutes
First performance: Eisenstadt, 13 September 1807
Soli, Chorus and Orchestra
Composer conducting

Complete orchestral parts compatible with this vocal score are available (Cat. No. A2558) from
E. F. Kalmus & Co., Inc.
6403 West Rogers Circle
Boca Raton, FL 33487 USA
(800) 434 - 6340
www.kalmus-music.com

Dem Fursten Ferdinand Kinsky gewidmet

Mass in C
Op. 86

1. Kyrie

Ludwig van Beethoven
Piano reduction by Carl Reinecke
Edited by Kurel Torvik

Copyright 2007 Serenissima Music, Inc.
All rights reserved. Printed in USA

2 beats

2. Gloria

2 beats

3. Credo

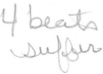

46

Z255891

4. Sanctus

4 beats

6. Agnus Dei